D1274792

PASCUALA HERRERA

ISBN: 978-1-7363388-4-1 (paperback)
ISBN: 978-1-7363388-5-8 (hardcover)

First Edition Book, September 2021

Book cover design, illustration, editing, and interior layout by:

www.1000storybooks.com

DEDICATION

To Ariel and Ariana - I learned to be a mom because of you!

My mom rocks;
her chair rolls.
I love her much
With all my soul.

XOX

Not on two feet

But on her seat

She is someone

You'd want to meet!

MOM

She loves me so much
She gives me big hugs
With her special touch
Alongside her I tug.

My mom is so cool
When we go for a spin.
If we were in a race,
We would both surely win.

When she zooms ‘cross the room
Wheeling round in her chair,
She smiles real wide—
The wind flies through her hair!

When little, she used
To play and be free,
But now she is grown
And has several degrees.

She not only helps me—
She helps others, too.
She teaches what she
And those like her can do.

PASSION
+
HARDWORK
=
SUCCESS
DON'T
STOP
UNTIL
YOU'RE
PROUD
DREAMS DO
NOT WORK
UNLESS YOU
DO!

When she travels for work,
In an airplane she flies.
And when she returns
She brings me a surprise.

She also can drive
In her shiny new car
To take me fun places
Both nearby and far.

She works long and hard
Both far and at home.
She sits on her wheels
Made from silvery chrome.

She does all of this
To make my life nice.
She is sweet as sugar
With twice the spice!

When we go to the mall
We shop like the rest.
Compared to them all
My mom is the best!

When we're in the store
I help her reach high.
I climb on her lap
'cause I'm such a small fry.

Chips
Chips

She cooks and prepares
Every one of my meals,
Holding pots and pans
While on her wheels.

I love when she makes
Macaroni and cheese.
She handles the kitchen
With style and ease.

Before I go play
And have my fun,
She helps me with homework
To make sure it’s done.

As she gives me a bath
I play in the bubbles.
I giggle and laugh
And I don’t give her troubles.

And when I get sick,
And things are not good,
She takes care of me well—
As all mommies should.

She takes me to the doctor,
Though I don't want to go.
She makes me feel good
By doing things *just so.*

She reads books to me
Each and every night
The voices she makes
Are out of sight!

At last, when it's late,
Before she turns off the light
She tucks me in bed
Very snugly and tight.

My mom rocks;
her chair rolls.
I love her much
With all my soul.

XOX

Not on two feet
But on her seat
She is someone
You'd want to meet!

BEST
MOM
MOM

About the Author

Pascuala Herrera is a Mexican immigrant woman with a disability due to childhood polio who currently uses a motorized wheelchair. She resides with her husband who also has a disability and two daughters. Pascuala worked as an educator for thirty years and published a memoir earlier in 2021. She is now a frequent local and national presenter on the topic of her life experience, disability awareness, motivation, and the importance of education for individuals with disabilities and Latinos.

CPSIA information can be obtained
at www.ICGtesting.com
Printed in the USA
LVHW050941221021
701097LV00002B/3

9 781736 338858